THE GOSPEL

God's Plan For Me

GOD RULES · WE SINNED · GOD PROVIDED · JESUS GIVES · WE RESPOND

D1614229

Older Kids Activity Book

CONTENTS

THE GOSPEL
God's Plan For Me

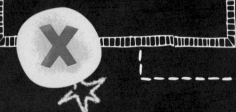

GOD RULES.

The Bible tells us God created everything, including you and me, and He is in charge of everything. Genesis 1:1; Revelation 4:11; Colossians 1:16-17

WE SINNED.

We all choose to disobey God. The Bible calls this sin. Sin separates us from God and deserves God's punishment of death. Romans 3:23; 6:23

GOD PROVIDED.

God sent Jesus, the perfect solution to our sin problem, to rescue us from the punishment we deserve. It's something we, as sinners, could never earn on our own. Jesus alone saves us. John 3:16; Ephesians 2:8-9

JESUS GIVES.

He lived a perfect life, died on the cross for our sins, and rose again. Because Jesus gave up His life for us, we can be welcomed into God's family for eternity. This is the best gift ever! Romans 5:8; 2 Cor. 5:21; 1 Peter 3:18; Ephesians 2:8-9

WE RESPOND.

Believe in your heart that Jesus alone saves you through what He's already done on the cross. Repent, turning from self and sin to Jesus. Tell God and others that your faith is in Jesus. John 14:6; Romans 10:9-10,13

GOD RULES.

When we grasp the gospel, we discover that God created everything through Jesus and for Jesus. God is Creator, God rules, and He loves us.

Key Points

When we grasp the gospel, we discover that...

- God created everything through Jesus and for Jesus.
- God is Creator.
- God rules.
- God loves us.

Key Verse

"Everything was created by him, in heaven and on earth, the visible and the invisible, whether thrones or dominions or rulers or authorities—all things have been created through him and for him. He is before all things, and by him all things hold together." Colossians 1:16-17 (CSB)

God Created the World

In the beginning, nothing existed except God. God spoke and created the heavens and the earth. When He first created the earth, it had no shape, and total darkness covered the earth. The Spirit of God was there, hovering over the waters. God spoke. He said, "Let there be light!" and what God said happened. Light was created. God saw that the light was good, and He separated the light from the darkness. God called the light day, and He called the darkness night. Evening came, and then morning. That was the first day of creation.

God spoke again: "Let there be an expanse between the waters, to separate them." What God said happened. He made a space between the water that was on the earth and the water above the earth. God called the expanse sky. Evening came, and then morning came. That was the second day of creation.

God said, "Let the water under the sky be gathered into one place, and let the dry land appear." What God said happened. God called the dry land earth, and He called the gathered water seas. God saw that it was good. Then God said, "Let the earth make plants and trees with fruits and seeds." What God said happened. Plants and trees grew, and God saw that it was good. Evening came, and then morning. That was the third day of creation.

Next, God placed lights in the sky. God created the sun to shine during the day and the moon and stars to shine at night. God gave us lights to provide light on the earth, to separate day from night, and to help us track time in days and years. God saw that it was good. Evening came, and then morning. That was the fourth day of creation.

Next, God made creatures that move and swim in the water. He made birds to flap their wings and soar across the sky. God saw that it was good. God told the animals to multiply, and they filled the seas and the sky. Evening came, and then morning. That was the fifth day of creation.

Then God made more animals—livestock, creatures that crawl, and wildlife to live on the earth. When God said it, it happened. And God saw that it was good.

—based on Genesis 1:1-25

God Rules.

Creator God

Turn to Genesis 1 and search the chapter for the word *God*.
Draw a tally mark for each time you see the word *God*.

What do you remember about creation?

_____

_____

"God saw that it was ◯◯◯◯ **."**

I've Spied

Look at each box and list the items you have seen that match
the days they were created.

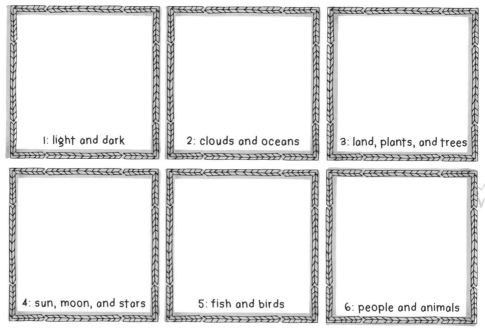

Day 7: God rested.

The Gospel: God's Plan—Older Kids Activity Book

Mad Lib® Prayer

Read the following prayer and write your answer from the words colored orange. Once you have written all your favorite answers, read your prayer.

Dear God,

You are an amazing Creator. There is no one like You. You

created _____ and _____ . You have
favorite flower   favorite animal

to be pretty creative to think up a _____ .
                                        a weird animal

You also created me, _____ . You also created
                        your name

me in Your image. That must mean You love me very much!

As I go through each day, help me to have eyes to see You

while I look at __Birds__ , __trutub__ , and
                something in the sky   something in the ocean

__Lizzy__ .
a friend's name

Because You made everything, You are in charge, and You hold

all things together. Help me to remember that.

In Jesus' name, amen.

Day One

Decode the words below to uncover an important reminder for the day. *Hint: Replace each number with its matching letter in the alphabet.*

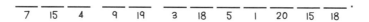

___ ___ ___ ___ ___ ___ ___ ___ ___ ___ ___ ___ .
 7 15   4   9 19   3 18 5   1 20 15 18

Read Revelation 4:11.

Looking at your Bible and using the hint above, decode the words in each blank.

Our ___ ___ ___ ___ and God, you are ___ ___ ___ ___ ___ ___ to
   12 15 18 4   23 15 18 20 8 25

receive glory and ___ ___ ___ ___ ___ and power, because you
            8 15 14 15 18

have ___ ___ ___ ___ ___ ___ ___ all things, and by your will they
   3 18 5 1 20 5 4

exist and were ___ ___ ___ ___ ___ ___ ___ . Revelation 4:11
        3 18 5 1 20 5 4

Who does the verse say is worthy to receive glory and honor and power?

_____

Why do you think God alone deserves such praise?

_____

On the lines below, list some of your favorite things that God created.

_____

_____

_____

Practice your key verse, Colossians 1:16-17, by reading it aloud.

Day Two

Replace each letter with the letter that comes after it in the alphabet. What is today's important reminder?

___ ___ ___ ___ ___ ___ ___ ___.
  F   N   C   Q   T   K   D   R

Which is your favorite part of a story, the beginning or the end?

_____

Open your Bible and read Genesis 1:1.

Who was here in the very beginning, and what did He create?

_____

What would you have created first?

_____

Unscramble the words and fill in the blanks to the key point. *Hint: you can look back a few pages.*

When we grasp the _____ , we discover that _____
                    legsop   oGd

created everything through _____ and for Jesus. God is
                             ssuJe

_____ , God _____ , and He _____ us.
   earCotr   urlse   sovle

Practice the key verse. Open your Bible to Colossians 1:16-17. Try to sing the verse to a familiar tune to help your memorize it!

Day Three

Unscramble the words to discover today's important truth.

_____ _____ _____ .
oGd   solev   em

Open your Bible to Colossians 1:16.

What was created by God?

_____

What is something we don't see that we know God created?

_____

Draw a picture of the most amazing thing you think God created.

Read Colossians 1:16 aloud five times. Do it once in a regular voice, once in slow motion, once in a whisper, once in an accent, and once without looking at your Bible.

Day Four

Read Colossians 1:17 in your Bible.

In the list below, circle which thing came first:

cat	kitten
seed	flower
adult	baby
flour	cookie
God	all things

How are things held together?

_____

Do you like to be in charge of things? _____

God is Creator and before all things. He made all things and holds them together. This is how we can know that God rules. Color the face that best represents how you feel to know that God rules and you do not.

Find a quiet place to pray. Ask God to help you trust Him and believe that He is in control of all things.

Day Five

This week we learned something special that God did when He created us: He made us in His image.

Open your Bible to Psalm 139:13-16 and read these verses aloud.

How does verse 14 say you are made? *Hint: Replace each number with its matching letter in the alphabet.*

—— —— —— —— —— —— —— —— —— ——
18   5   13   1   18   11   1   2   12   25

&   —— —— —— —— —— —— —— —— —— ——
     23   15   14   4   5   18   6   21   12   12   25

Whose works are wondrous (wonderful)? _____

Never forget that God created you and loves you very much. He saw you when you were formless. He loves you too much to let you be in charge. He is Creator and holds all things together. When we grasp the gospel, we discover the God who created all is in charge and we are not.

Try reciting the key verse, Colossians 1:16-17, to a family member by memory.

A journal is a place to keep track of your thoughts, feelings, questions, answers, and prayers. Use this page to write down what God is teaching you, any questions you have, or what you want to talk to God about.

WE SINNED.

When we grasp the gospel, we discover that we are sinners and our sin separates us from God.

Key Points

When we grasp the gospel, we discover that...

- Sin is anything we think, say, or do that displeases God.

- We are sinners.

- Our sin separates us from God.

- God cannot ignore and must punish our sin.

Key Verse

"All have sinned and fall short of the glory of God."
Romans 3:23 (CSB)

The Gospel: God's Plan—Older Kids Activity Book

Sin Entered the World

God gave the first two people, Adam and Eve, a beautiful garden to live in. The garden was full of food they could eat. God also gave them one command. He told Adam that he could eat from any tree in the garden except for one. It was called the tree of the knowledge of good and evil. God said that if Adam did eat from the tree, he would die.

Now the serpent was the most cunning of all the animals. One day, the serpent went to Eve. He asked, "Did God really say, 'You can't eat from any tree in the garden'?" Eve answered, "We can eat the fruit from the trees in the garden. But God told us not to eat from the tree in the middle of the garden. He said that if we eat the fruit or touch it, we will die."

"No! You will not die," the serpent said. The serpent told Eve that rather than dying, she and Adam would be like God! They would know good and evil. Eve looked at the fruit God had said not to eat. It did look delicious, and the serpent said it would give them wisdom. So she took some of the fruit and ate it. Eve also gave some of the fruit to Adam, who was with her, and he ate it.

Then their eyes were opened, and they knew they were naked. Adam and Eve sewed together fig leaves and made clothes for themselves. That evening, Adam and Eve heard God walking in the garden. They hid among the trees. God called out to Adam, "Where are you?" Adam said, "I was afraid because I was naked, so I hid." God asked Adam, "Who told you that you were naked? Did you eat from the tree that I commanded you not to eat from?" Adam blamed Eve. "She gave me some fruit from the tree, and I ate it," he said. Eve blamed the serpent. "He tricked me," she said.

God said that because of the serpent's trick and Adam and Eve's disobedience, bad things would happen. Eve would have more pain when she had children, and Adam would struggle to work the ground for food. God said that the snake would crawl on its belly and be an enemy to the woman. But God promised that one of Eve's descendants would destroy the serpent. Everything changed after Adam and Eve sinned. Sin separated Adam and Eve from God. God made them clothes out of animal skins and then sent them out of the garden. God put an angel at the entrance of the garden. The angel had a sword of fire to guard the way to the tree of life.

—based on Genesis 3:1-24

We Sinned.

THINK, SAY, or DO

Sin is anything we think, say, or do that displeases God. As you think of different sins, list them in the column they fit in best. Try to list at least two for each category.

Circle/Square Review

The statements listed below are about the true story you just heard in Genesis 3. After you read the statement, if you believe it is true, fill in the circle. If you believe the statement is not true, cross through the square.

1. The story in Genesis 3 is just a fable and never really happened.

2. God gave so many commands to Adam and Eve in the garden that they couldn't remember them all.

3. The tree they couldn't eat from was called the tree of knowledge of good and evil.

4. If they ate from this tree, they would die.

○ ☐ 5. The serpent was on God's team and was trying to help Eve.

○ ☐ 6. The serpent spoke truth to Eve, and he could be trusted. ☆

○ ☐ 7. The serpent made Eve eat the fruit.

○ ☐ 8. Adam refused to eat the fruit.

○ ☐ 9. When God came to the garden, Adam and Eve ran to meet Him.

○ ☐ 10. God said He would just ignore the fact that Adam and Eve disobeyed Him.

○ ☐ 11. Everything changed after Adam and Eve sinned.

○ ☐ 12. Sin separated Adam and Eve from God.

○ ☐ 13. Adam and Eve's disobedience doesn't affect us today.

○ ☐ 14. We are all sinners and fall short of God's perfect standard.

☆ **PUNISH OR NOT?**

Draw your favorite possession and answer the following questions.

1. How do you feel about the possession you drew? 😄 🙂 😐 🙁

2. How would you feel if someone destroyed your picture? 😄 🙂 😐 🙁

3. How would you feel if someone actually destroyed your favorite possession, not just a picture of it? 😄 🙂 😐 🙁

4. How would you feel if no one punished him for what he did to your real possession? 😄 🙂 😐 🙁

5. Do you think he needs to be punished? 😄 🙂 😐 🙁

My Favorite Possession

We Sinned.

Day One

Do you remember what the word *sin* means? Fill in the blanks using the words we used to define sin on page 18 of this book.

Sin is anything we _____ , _____ , or _____ that displeases God.

What is one thing you thought, said, or did today that didn't please God?

_____

How did you feel after you sinned? _____

Open your Bible and read this week's key verse, Romans 3:23. Using your Bible, fill in the missing word in the verse.

"_____ have sinned and fall short of the glory of God."

Circle all the people below that have sinned according to this verse.

meanest kid
in school

you

your
pastor

nicest person
you know

your
teacher

your
parents

This week's key verse tells us that we have *all* sinned and fall short of the glory of God. That means *everyone* has sinned, even the best person you know. This is an important truth of the gospel, because we must know we have sinned to understand we need to be rescued.

Day Two

Look back to page 6 and see if you can fill in the words to the key point.

When we grasp the _____ , we discover that _____ created everything through _____ and for Jesus. God is _____ , God _____ , and He _____ us.

Decode the words below and write in the missing words to this week's main point. *Hint: Replace each number with its matching letter in the alphabet.*

When we grasp the _ _ _ _ _ _ _ , we discover that we are
  7 15 19 16 5 12

_ _ _ _ _ _ _ and our sin _ _ _ _ _ _ _ _ _ _ us from God.
19 9 14 14 5 18 19   19 5 16 1 18 1 20 5 19 .

Open your Bible to Romans 3:23. Read the first part of the verse (the first four words).

God

Romans 3:23 says we fall short of God. Look at this picture. If God is high up, and we fall short of His standard, write your name on the picture where you think you are compared to God. Why did you put your name where you did?

Practice this week's key verse by reading it aloud in different positions. Check off each one as you have completed it. "All have sinned and fall short of the glory of God." Romans 3:23 (CSB)

☐ Standing tall.   ☐ Jumping on one foot.

☐ Running in place.   ☐ Lying on your back.

Day Three

How does it make you feel to hear that you are a sinner? Draw a face showing how you feel in the circle.

Read Romans 6:23 aloud.
Answer the questions below based on what you read. Choose the answers in the word bank that fits best in each blank.

What is our payment for sin? _____

What is the gift of God? _____ _____

Who is the gift through? _____ _____

How does it make you feel to know God doesn't leave you as a sinner, but sends help? Draw a face showing how you feel in the circle.

Practice Romans 3:23 by writing in the first part of the verse.

"_____ have _____ and

_____ short of the glory of God."

Romans 3:23 (CSB)

Day Four

Open your Bible and read James 4:17. This verse tells us that it is a sin to know good and then not to do it. Sometimes we like to think sin is a mistake because it makes us feel better. Write the verse large in the space below.

_____

_____

_____

Sin is not a mistake; sin is a choice. Let's see if you know the difference between a mistake and a choice. Circle the mistakes below and put an *X* on top of the sins.

Accidentally dropping a jar and breaking it

Taking a cookie when your mom told you to wait until after dinner

Forgetting your homework at home

Disobeying your parents

Telling your parents you don't have homework when you know you do

Saying something mean to someone

Practice Romans 3:23 by writing in the second part of the verse.

"All have sinned and fall _____ of the _____

of _____ ." Romans 3: _____ (CSB)

Day Five

Open your Bible to Romans 3:10 and read the verse aloud.
What does this verse say about sin? Write it in the speech
bubble below.

God's Word is clear that we are sinners. That is bad news; but
the good news of the gospel is that God doesn't leave us as
sinners if we come to Him.

Turn in your Bible to I John 1:9 and read this verse.

Confess means to agree with God. This verse teaches us that if
we agree with God that we are a sinner, He is faithful to forgive
our sin and cleanse us from unrighteousness.

After all that we have learned this week, how do you see
yourself? Mark where you see yourself on the scale below using
an *X*.

Perfect   Maybe I sin.   Sinner

Why did you put your mark where you did?

_____

_____

_____

Practice this week's key verse by saying it to a family member.
See if he or she can repeat it back to you.

A journal is a place to keep track of your thoughts, feelings, questions, answers, and prayers. Use this page to write down what God is teaching you, any questions you have, or what you want to talk to God about.

GOD PROVIDED.

When we grasp the gospel, we discover that God provided a way for us to be saved by grace through faith in Christ alone.

Key Points

When we grasp the gospel, we discover that...

- Sin created a problem we cannot solve on our own.

- God provided the solution to our sin problem.

- Through faith in Jesus Christ alone, we can be rescued from our sin.

Key Verse

"For God loved the world in this way: He gave his one and only Son, so that everyone who believes in him will not perish but have eternal life." John 3:16 (CSB)

The Woman at the Well

Jesus had been making disciples in Judea, and His disciples baptized people. Now Jesus had more followers than John the Baptist. Jesus began traveling back to Galilee. He traveled through Samaria and stopped in a town at the well. Jesus' disciples went into town to buy food.

While Jesus was at the well, a Samaritan woman came to get water from the well. "Give Me a drink," Jesus said to the woman. The woman was surprised. "You're a Jew," she said. "Why are You talking to me? I'm a Samaritan."

Jesus said, "I asked you for a drink. You don't know who I am. If you did, you would have asked me for a drink, and I would give you living water." The woman was confused. "Sir," she said, "This well is deep, and you don't have a bucket. Where do you get this 'living water'?"

Jesus said, "Anyone who drinks this well water will be thirsty again, but whoever drinks from the water I give will never, ever get thirsty again! In fact, the water I give will become a well inside you, and you will have eternal life." Jesus was talking about the Holy Spirit, but the woman did not understand.

"Sir," she said, "give me this water. If I'm not thirsty, I won't have to keep coming to this well to get water." "Go get your husband," Jesus said. "I don't have a husband," the woman replied. Jesus knew she was telling the truth. He said, "You don't have a husband now, but you've had five husbands."

Jesus was right. "I see you are a prophet," the woman said. Maybe this prophet could explain something to her. She said, "The Samaritans worship here on a mountain, but the Jews say we need to worship at the temple in Jerusalem."

Jesus said, "Soon you will not need to be in either of those places to worship God in spirit and in truth." The woman said, "I know the Messiah is coming. When He comes, He will explain everything to us."

Then Jesus said, "He is talking to you now. I am the Messiah." The woman left and told the people in her town, "Come, see a man who told me everything I ever did! Could this be the Messiah?"

Many Samaritans believed in Jesus because of what the woman said. They asked Jesus to stay with them, and He stayed for two days. Many more believed because of what Jesus said. They told the woman, "We no longer believe because of what you said, for we have heard for ourselves and know that this really is the Savior of the world."

—based on John 4:1-42

God Provided.

John 3:16 Illustrated

Read the words of John 3:16 and color the words as you go. Then draw an image this verse makes you think about.

The Gospel: God's Plan—Older Kids Activity Book

Living Water

Follow your leader's instructions to complete this activity.

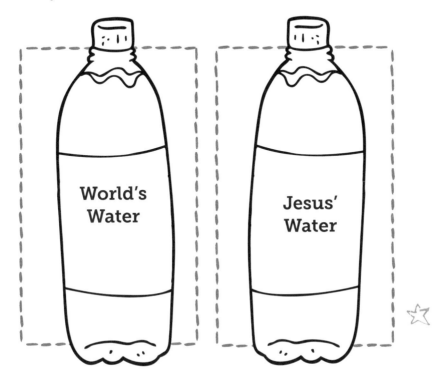

World's
Water

Jesus'
Water

What is Grace?

Complete the definition for grace based on what you have learned today.

Grace is when we _____ a _____

we _____ deserve.

God Provided.

Day One

Write each of the provided words in the correct blank in the main point.

When we grasp the _____ , we discover that
God _____ a way to be _____ by
_____ through _____ in Christ alone.

gospel   sin   provided   problem   solution   faith

Open your Bible to John 3:16 and read this verse aloud. You may be very familiar with this verse, but we want to look more closely at what this verse says. Answer the questions below.

Why did God act in this verse?

_____

What did God give?

_____

What does He call us to do?

_____

What does God give us?

_____

Who is His gift through?

_____

This week's memory verse is John 3:16. Read this verse aloud three times, then have a family member read it to you three times aloud. Try to say it from memory with this family member. (Yes, you can look at the Bible if you need help!)

Day Two

Fill in the blank about grace. Look on page 29 for a hint!

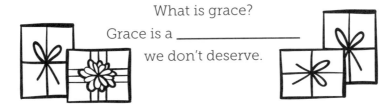

What is grace?

Grace is a _____

we don't deserve.

Open your Bible to John 1:14 and read this verse aloud. Answer the questions below by looking at this verse for the correct answers.

Who is the Word that became flesh and dwelt among us? Replace each letter with the letter that comes before it in the alphabet.

___ ___ ___ ___ ___
K   F   T   V   T

Who was He sent from?

___ ___ ___   ___ ___ ___   ___ ___ ___ ___ ___ ___ ___
H P E   U I F   G B U I F S

What was He full of? _____ and _____

God the Father provided His Son. Jesus is full of grace and truth. That's pretty amazing news! What else do you know about Jesus? List anything you know about Jesus on the lines below.

_____

_____

_____

Practice saying the key verse for this week. Make up motions to John 3:16. Practice reading the verse and doing the motions with a friend or sibling (brother or sister).

Day Three

Read the actions in each box. Imagine you completed each of these, then draw a picture in the space provided of what kind of reward or payment you think you should receive.

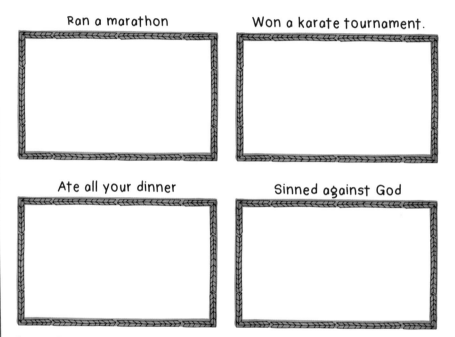

Ran a marathon

Won a karate tournament.

Ate all your dinner

Sinned against God

In each of these listed accomplishments, there was a reward or payment someone deserved. The one that is the hardest for us to grasp is that our sin deserves the payment of death. But God provided so much more. He gave us Jesus. What do you think about God providing His one and only Son to pay the price for our sin? Write Him a letter telling Him how you feel or asking Him any questions.

_____

_____

Day Four

Open your Bible to John 4:1-42. Read these verses with an adult or reread the story of the woman at the well on page 27. Draw what you think of when you read that story.

Did this woman deserve an appointment at the well with Jesus?

Yes No

Did Jesus give her living water because she earned it?

Yes No

This true story of Jesus meeting with a sinful woman is a wonderful picture of grace. This woman had a sin problem that she could not solve on her own. She needed to be rescued from her sin problem through faith in Jesus.

See if you can fill in the missing words below without looking up the verse.

"For God loved the _____ in this way: He gave his one

and only _____ , so that _____ who believes in him

will not _____ but have _____ life." John 3:16 (CSB)

God provided the solution to our sin problem through faith in Christ alone.

Day Five

Circle the bubble of the person who is boasting.

> Thank you for your compliment! I tried my best.

> Yeah, I know I am the best. I won that game for my whole team.

> Oh, who me? I didn't do that well.

How do you feel about people that boast or brag? _____

_____

When we boast or brag, we focus more on ourselves than what really matters. That's why this week's key verse, John 3:16, reminds us that we can't save ourselves, so we can't brag about it. God provided the perfect solution to our sin problem through Jesus.

Read John 3:16 in your Bible.

Who is the only One who can save us? _____

_____

Who provided our Savior? _____

_____

What does Jesus rescue us from? _____

_____

A journal is a place to keep track of your thoughts, feelings, questions, answers, and prayers. Use this page to write down what God is teaching you, any questions you have, or what you want to talk to God about.

_____

_____

_____

_____

_____

_____

_____

_____

_____

_____

JESUS GIVES.

When we grasp the gospel, we discover that Jesus gave up His perfect life and died on the cross to pay the price for our sin.

Key Points

When we grasp the gospel, we discover that...

- Jesus lived a perfect life.
- Jesus willingly gave His life for us by dying on the cross for our sins.
- Mercy is when we don't receive what we deserve.
- Jesus didn't stay dead. He defeated death and rose again.

Key Verse

"God proves his own love for us in that while we were still sinners, Christ died for us." Romans 5:8 (CSB)

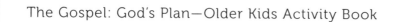

Jesus' Crucifixion and Resurrection

Jesus came with His disciples to Gethsemane (geth-SEM-uh-nih). While Jesus prayed, the disciples fell asleep. Jesus said, "Get up. It is almost time." Suddenly, Judas arrived with a large crowd. Judas kissed Jesus so the crowd would know who Jesus was. The crowd grabbed Jesus and arrested Him. Peter tried to stop the men, but Jesus told Peter to stop. Jesus' followers ran away, but Peter stayed nearby.

Jesus was led to the high priest. The religious leaders tried to find a reason to kill Jesus, but they could not. The high priest asked, "Are you the Messiah, the Son of God? Jesus replied, "Yes, that's right."

The high priest said, "Aha! He has spoken against God. He deserves to die!" The religious leaders did not want to believe Jesus was God's Son. They led Jesus to Pilate, the governor. "Are you the king of the Jews?" Pilate asked. "Yes, that's right," Jesus replied. "What should I do with Jesus?" Pilate asked the crowd. "Crucify Him!" they said. Pilate did not think Jesus had done anything wrong, but he handed Jesus over.

The soldiers put a scarlet robe and a crown of thorns on Jesus. Then they mocked Him, "Here is the king of the Jews!" They beat Jesus and led Him away to be killed. The soldiers nailed Jesus to a cross. They put a sign above His head that said THIS IS JESUS, THE KING OF THE JEWS.

Darkness covered the land. Then Jesus cried out, "My God, My God, why have You abandoned Me?" Jesus shouted again and then He died. Suddenly, the curtain in the temple sanctuary split in two, from top to bottom, and there was an earthquake. One of the men guarding Jesus' body said, "This man really was God's Son!"

Jesus was buried in a tomb. A stone was sealed in front of the tomb so that no one could steal Jesus' body. On the third day, Mary Magdalene (MAG duh leen) and the other Mary went to the tomb. Suddenly there was an earthquake. An angel of the Lord rolled back the stone. The angel spoke to the women, "Don't be afraid! I know you are looking for Jesus, but He is not here. He has been resurrected, just like He said He would. In fact, He is going ahead of you into Galilee."

The women hurried to tell the disciples the good news. Just then Jesus met them. "Good morning!" He said. The women worshiped Him. "Don't be afraid," Jesus told them. "Go tell My disciples to meet Me in Galilee. They will see Me there."

—based on Matthew 26:36–28:10; John 18:1–20:18

Jesus Gives.

Grace or Mercy?

Read each statement. Circle which word you think that statement best represents—*grace* or *mercy*. Then answer the two questions at the bottom of the activity.

> *Grace* is when we receive a gift we don't deserve.
> *Mercy* is when we don't receive what we do deserve.

1. Peter did not eat all his dinner, but his parents allowed him to have ice cream for dessert.   **Grace**   **Mercy**

2. Sally disobeyed her parents when they were at a friend's house, and that usually means she is punished at home. Sally's parents chose not to punish her when she got home.
Grace   **Mercy**

3. Tim got sick and couldn't help much with his group project for school. His team members took on extra jobs so that Tim's name could still be on the project.   **Grace**   **Mercy**

4. Emily had a very difficult week at home and scored poorly on a test at school. Instead of getting a bad grade, the teacher allowed her one more night to study.
Grace   **Mercy**

5. The last time Bobby used his dad's tools, he didn't put them up correctly and one was broken. Bobby's dad decided to give him another chance and allowed him to use his tools.
Grace   **Mercy**

How did God show us grace? _____

How did Jesus show us mercy? _____

To The Rescue

Read each statement and draw a line to the rescuer you would want for the situation.

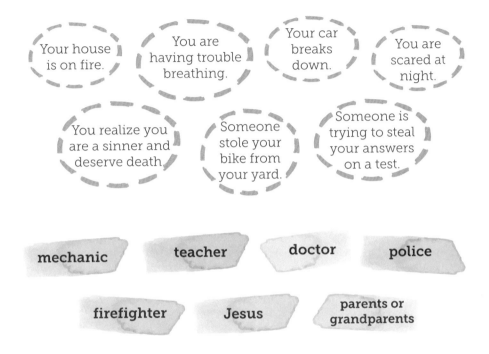

Your house is on fire.

You are having trouble breathing.

Your car breaks down.

You are scared at night.

You realize you are a sinner and deserve death.

Someone stole your bike from your yard.

Someone is trying to steal your answers on a test.

mechanic   **teacher**   **doctor**   **police**

firefighter   **Jesus**   **parents or grandparents**

Alive or Not?

Underneath each portrait write whether you think this hero is still alive or not here anymore.

Moses

Esther

Noah

David

Jesus

Ruth

Jesus Gives.

Day One

What is something you do that makes you not perfect?

_____

Jesus was perfect, and He never sinned. That is pretty amazing, isn't it? Circle which question you would like to ask Jesus about living a perfect life:

- Was it hard being perfect?

- What did your family think about You being perfect?

- Why did you love us so much to give your perfect life for us?

Not only was Jesus perfect, but He also gave His life for us. We learn that is one way—the best way!—God proved His love for us.

Open your Bible to Romans 5:8. Fill in the missing words in your key verse below.

"_____ proves his own _____ for us

in that while we were still _____,

_____ died for us." Romans 5:8 (CSB)

Say this verse aloud three times to someone in your family today. Try writing it in your own words below.

_____

_____

_____

_____

Day Two

Draw a line from the object to the price you think best fits it.

New Car	$130.00
Gaming System	Death
Ice Cream	$300.00
Sin	$35,000
Hotel night	$5.00

Which item costs the most in your opinion?

_____

Read Romans 5:8 in your Bible. Sin separates us from God, so a high price must be paid to repair our relationship with Jesus. God proved He loved us by doing what? *(Hint: The answer is found in the key verse this week, Romans 5:8.)*

"God proves his own love for us in that while we were

still sinners, _____ _____ _____

_____ ." Romans 5:8 (CSB)

What does it mean to you that God paid such a high price for your sin?

_____

_____

_____

Day Three

We learned this week that *mercy* is when we don't get something we deserve. Do you remember a time in your life where you were shown mercy? **Yes   No**

If so, what does it feel like to be shown mercy? _____

Break the code to discover the punishment we deserved but Jesus took for us:

___ ___ ___ ___ ___
A+3 H-3 Z-25 S+1 J-2

Open your Bible to 2 Corinthians 5:21 and read this verse. The words to this verse are provided below, but they are not in the right order. Unscramble them and write the verse correctly below.

> become He one God who did that not might sin to sin us,
> so in him we know the for righteousness the of made be

_____

_____

_____

Jesus took on all our sin. That was a heavy load, but He did it because He loves us. The key verse tells us that was how He proved His love for us.

Try filling out the key verse below without looking it up in your Bible.

"God _____ his own _____ for _____ in that while we were still _____, Christ died for _____." Romans 5:8 (CSB)

Day Four

This week we learned that when we grasp the gospel, we discover that Jesus gave up His perfect life and died on the cross to pay the price for our sin.

Jesus showed us mercy by taking the punishment we deserve for sin. Do you remember what mercy means? Look back to page 38 and unscramble the definition below.

don't receive is we

deserve what do Mercy we when

_____

_____

_____

Open your Bible and read 1 Peter 3:18.

What does it say Christ suffered? _____

Why did He suffer? _____

Christ suffered for sin and He did it to bring you to God. God doesn't want us to stay separated from Him in our sin.

God

Us

Draw a cross to connect God and us. Jesus is the answer for our sin problem.

Day Five

Open your Bible to John 20. Read John 20:11-18 on your own or with an adult. After reading, answer the following questions.

Did Jesus die on the cross for our sins?   Yes   No

Is He alive today?   Yes   No

How did Mary Magdalene react when she saw Jesus?
she didn't care   she hid   she announced she had seen the Lord

How would you react if you saw Jesus after you had seen Him crucified?
be scared   cry   hug Him   act excited

Not only did Jesus die for our sins, but He is alive today! We may not see Him with our eyes, but God's Word gives us proof He is alive. Mary couldn't wait to tell the news that Jesus was alive.

Who can you tell that amazing news to? _____

Try saying the key verse to someone in your family. If you can, say it without looking. See if you can write the verse below from memory.

A journal is a place to keep track of your thoughts, feelings, questions, answers, and prayers. Use this page to write down what God is teaching you, any questions you have, or what you want to talk to God about.

WE RESPOND.

When we grasp the gospel, we discover that God's gift of Jesus is the only way to be saved. To receive this gift, we must believe in our hearts that Jesus saves us by the work He has already done on the cross.

Key Points

When we grasp the gospel, we discover that...

- There is only one way to be saved—Jesus.

- Jesus, the gift of God, is the greatest gift we have ever been given, but we must respond to receive this gift.

- We can be welcomed into God's family by believing in our hearts that Jesus saves us by what He has already done on the cross.

Key Verse

"If you confess with your mouth, 'Jesus is Lord,' and believe in your heart that God raised him from the dead, you will be saved." Romans 10:9 (CSB)

Jesus Met Nicodemus

Jesus had traveled to Jerusalem for the Passover feast. One night, a religious man came to see Jesus. The man's name was Nicodemus. Nicodemus was a Pharisee. He studied and taught God's law, and he tried very hard to obey the law. Nicodemus wanted to know more about Jesus.

"Rabbi," he said, "we know that You have come from God. You are a teacher, and no one could do the miracles You do unless God is with him."

Nicodemus had that right. Jesus said, "I tell you: Unless someone is born again, he cannot see the kingdom of God."

Now Nicodemus was confused. He thought that keeping all God's laws was how a person got into heaven. Besides, what Jesus said didn't make any sense! "How can anyone be born when he is old?" Nicodemus asked.

Jesus said, "A man cannot enter God's kingdom unless he is born of water and the Spirit. Whatever is born of the flesh is flesh, and whatever is born of the Spirit is spirit." When a baby is born, he gets physical life from his parents. Physical life doesn't last forever. But the Spirit gives people spiritual life so they can live with God forever.

Jesus said, "Don't be surprised I told you that you must be born again." Nicodemus still didn't understand. "How is this possible?" he asked.

Jesus replied, "We talk about what we know, and we tell others about what we have seen. But you don't believe what I'm telling you! When you don't believe what I say about things I've seen on earth, how will you believe what I say about the things I've seen in heaven?

"No one has ever gone up into heaven, except the Son of man. He came down from heaven. Do you remember how Moses raised up the bronze snake in the wilderness? Everyone who looked at it was healed. Like that, the Son of Man will be raised up, so that everyone who believes in Him will have eternal life."

Then Jesus told Nicodemus about God's great plan. Jesus said, "God showed His love in this way: He sent His One and Only Son to save the world. Everyone who believes in Him will not perish but will have eternal life.

"God didn't send His Son to declare the world guilty, but to save the world. Anyone who believes in Him is found not guilty, but anyone who does not believe in Him is guilty already."

–based on John 3:1-21

We Respond.

One Way Maze

Beginning in the middle, try to draw a line from you to God.

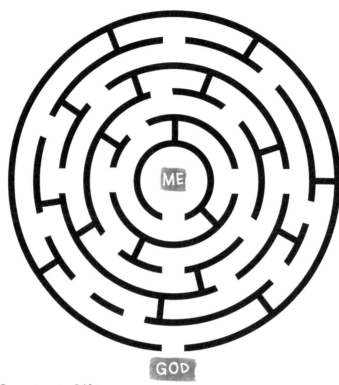

The Greatest Gift

In the box, write or draw something you think would be the most amazing gift to receive.

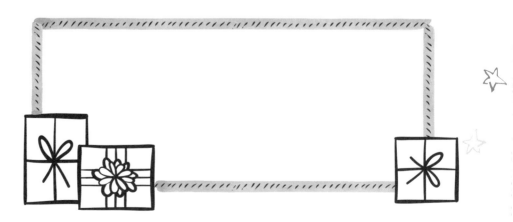

Even after hearing about Jesus, many people choose not to respond to this great gift of God. Circle some of the reasons you think people don't respond.

They don't think they need Jesus.

They think church is enough.

They can't find the gift.

They don't like gift.

The gift is just too good to be true.

They are trusting in something else to save them.

They have been taught something else their whole lives.

They don't believe in Him.

They just try to obey all the laws.

Prayer Journal

After hearing these great truths today, respond by writing a prayer to God.

Dear God,

_____

_____

_____

_____

_____

_____

In Jesus' name, amen.

We Respond.

Day One

On each question below, circle your favorite answer.

Favorite sport?	Football	Baseball	Soccer
Favorite food?	Hot Dogs	Pizza	Hamburgers
Favorite dessert?	Ice Cream	Cookies	Cake

Was it easy or hard for you just to pick one thing? Easy Hard

Sometimes we have trouble picking just one. What if we like other things, too? Having a tie for first might be OK in sport and food questions, but there is a special place where only one answer will do.

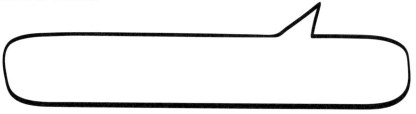

Open your Bibles to John 14:6. In this verse, Jesus is speaking. Write the important message that Jesus had to share in the speech bubble coming out of His mouth.

How many ways did Jesus say there was to God the Father? *Circle your answer.*   3   2   I   5

Who must you go through to get to God the Father? *Circle your answer.*   Jesus   Nicodemus   a Pastor

Open your Bible to Romans 10:9. This is the key verse for the week.

Read it once very slowly, then try to read it a little faster. Read this verse very quietly, then read it loudly. Try to memorize this verse for the week.

Day Two

God gave us the greatest gift we could ever receive. Color in the spaces with the gray dots to reveal the picture below.

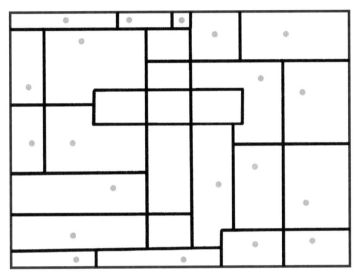

God gave us Jesus, but some people never choose to open that gift. If they do not respond, the gift is never theirs.

Open your Bible to Romans 10:13 and read this verse aloud.

What must you do to be saved? _____

Who does God save? _____

See if you can fill in the words to this week's memory verse without looking. There are symbols to help you.

"If you confess with your _____ , "_____ , is

Lord," and believe in your _____ , that God raised him

from the dead, you will be saved." Romans 10:9 (CSB)

Day Three

Unscramble the words below to read the key point.

When we _____ the _____ , we discover that God's
           prgso   lopegs
gift of _____ is the only way to be saved. To receive this
           sJuse
gift we must _____ in our _____ that Jesus saves
           ebeeivl   sertha
us by the work He has already done on the _____ .
                                             rcsso

What has Jesus done on the cross for you and me? _____

Open your Bible to Romans 10:9-10. Read these verses aloud and
then answer the following questions.

What must you confess with your mouth? _____

_____

What must you believe in your heart? _____

_____

What does the Bible say will happen if you confess with your
mouth that Jesus is Lord and believe in your heart that God
raised Him from the dead? _____

_____

Look at Romans 10:9 in your Bible. Read it once aloud, then close
your Bible and try to say the verse from memory.

Day Four

List three fun facts about your family.

_____

_____

_____

What do you think is something amazing about being part of God's family? _____

_____

Open your Bible to Galatians 3:26 and read this verse aloud.

We are welcomed into God's family when we respond to the gospel by placing our faith in what Jesus has already done on the cross.

Draw a picture of people you know who are Christians and part of God's family.

Open your Bible to Romans 10:9. Take your Bible to a family member and have him check while you try to say the key verse aloud.

Day Five

Open your Bible to John 3:1-21. Read the story of Nicodemus with an adult, or read the story provided on page 47. If the statements below are true, put a smiley face beside them. If they are false, put a sad face beside them.

☐ Nicodemus wanted to learn more about Jesus.

☐ Nicodemus did not know true things about God.

☐ You don't have to be born again to enter the kingdom of heaven.

☐ Jesus told Nicodemus about God's great plan.

☐ God sent His Son into the world to save the world.

Think about all the true things you know about God. List some of those truths on the lines below.

_____

_____

Did you know that we can know true things about God, but not have a relationship with Him? Nicodemus was a very smart, religious man. He knew all about God, but he didn't have a personal relationship with God through Jesus. Jesus taught Nicodemus about God's great plan—salvation through Jesus!

Write a prayer asking God to help you understand more about His plan to send Jesus for you.

_____

_____

_____

A journal is a place to keep track of your thoughts, feelings, questions, answers, and prayers. Use this page to write down what God is teaching you, any questions you have, or what you want to talk to God about.

THE GOSPEL AND ME.

When we grasp the gospel, we discover that God Rules, We Sinned, God Provided, Jesus Gives, and We Respond. These gospel truths are personal, life-changing, and can make us into a new creation.

Key Points

When we grasp the gospel, we discover that...

- The good news is: God Rules, We Sinned, God Provided, Jesus Gives, and We Respond.

- In Christ we are new creations; the old has gone the new has come.

- We can't keep this news to ourselves; we have to share the good news of Jesus with others.

Key Verse

"Therefore, if anyone is in Christ, he is a new creation; the old has passed away, and see, the new has come!" 2 Corinthians 5:17 (CSB)

Paul's Conversion and Baptism

After Jesus died, rose from the dead, and ascended to heaven, people in Jerusalem who believed in Jesus were persecuted, or treated cruelly because of their faith. One of Jesus' followers, Stephen, was even killed. A man named Saul had been there when Stephen was killed. Saul wanted to put an end to the church. He went into the believers' homes, dragged them out, and put them into jail. Many believers fled the city.

Saul headed to Damascus (duh-MASS-kuhs) to arrest believers there, but on the way, a bright light from heaven suddenly flashed around him. Saul fell to the ground. He heard a voice saying, "Saul, Saul, why are you persecuting Me?"

"Who are You, Lord?" Saul asked. "I am Jesus," He replied. "Get up and go into the city. Then you will be told what you must do." Saul got up and opened his eyes, but he couldn't see! So the men who were traveling with Saul led him by the hand into Damascus.

Ananias (an-uh-NIGH-uhs), a disciple of Jesus, lived in Damascus. The Lord spoke to Ananias in a vision. He told him to go to the house where Saul was staying. Ananias knew that Saul had hurt many believers in Jerusalem and that he arrested anyone who believed in Jesus. But the Lord said, "Go! I have chosen this man to take My name to Gentiles, kings, and the Israelites."

Ananias obeyed the Lord. He found Saul and told Saul that Jesus had sent him to help. Ananias put his hands on Saul, and suddenly Saul could see again. Saul got up and was baptized.

For the next few days, Saul stayed with the believers in Damascus. He began to go to the synagogues to preach about Jesus. Saul told the people, "Jesus is the Son of God!" The people were amazed. They recognized Saul and knew he had wanted to put an end to the church and all the believers. Now he was one of them! The Jews did not like Saul's message, so they planned to kill him. Saul heard what the Jews wanted to do, so one night he left the city. The disciples helped Saul escape by lowering him down the city wall in a basket.

—based on Acts 9:1-25

The Gospel and Me.

Stairwell Gospel

Take a look at the stairwell diagram on this page. As your leader walks you through the diagram, label each part.

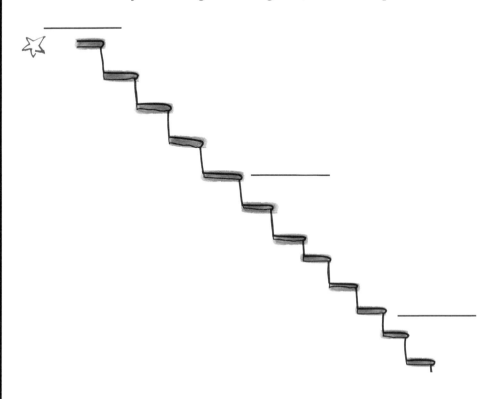

_____

_____

_____

What are some things people think they can do to save themselves from sin?

_____

_____

_____

_____

What did you learn in this activity?

_____

_____

_____

New Creations

Look at the two pictures below. Look at the two pictures below. Color only the spaces with the gray dots in them. • One dot is red, •• two dots is green, ••• three dots is yellow.

Gospel in Your Own Words

How would you explain the gospel—the good news of Jesus—in your own words? Write out the gospel in your own words below.

_____

_____

_____

_____

The Gospel and Me.

Day One

GOD RULES.

When we grasp the gospel, we discover that God created everything through Jesus and for Jesus. God is Creator, God rules, and He loves us.

Interview someone in your family that is a Christian. Ask the following questions and record the answers in your own words.

Family Member's Name _____

What is your favorite part of God's creation?_____
_____

How do you know God is the Creator? _____
_____

How does it make you feel to know God is in charge and you are not?
_____

How have you felt God's love this week? _____
_____

How has the gospel changed your life?_____
_____

Day Two

WE SINNED.

When we grasp the gospel, we discover that we are sinners, and our sin separates us from God.

Interview a church staff member (not your pastor). Ask the following questions and record the answers in your own words.

Staff Member's Name _____

How would you explain sin? _____

_____

How do you know that you are a sinner? _____

_____

How does your sin make you feel? _____

_____

How have you felt God's love this week? _____

_____

How has the gospel changed your life? _____

_____

Day Three

GOD PROVIDED.

When we grasp the gospel, we discover that God provided the solution to our sin problem through faith in Christ alone.

Interview a grandparent, aunt/uncle, or cousin who is a Christian. Ask the following questions and record the answers.

Family Member's Name _____

How do you feel about God's gift of Jesus?_____

_____

What does grace mean to you?_____

_____

How do you live your life by faith? _____

_____

How have you felt God's love this week? _____

_____

How has the gospel changed your life?_____

_____

Day Four

JESUS GIVES.

When we grasp the gospel, we discover that Jesus gave up His perfect life and died on the cross to pay the price for our sins.

Interview a church leader or teacher that is a Christian. Ask the following questions and record the answers in your own words.

Church Leader's Name _____

Explain what it means to you that Jesus gave His life for you.

_____

_____

What does mercy mean to you? _____

_____

What comes to mind when you think about Jesus dying on the cross?

_____

How have you felt God's love this week? _____

_____

How has the gospel changed your life? _____

_____

Day Five

WE RESPOND.

When we grasp the gospel, we discover that God's gift of Jesus is the only way to be saved. To receive this gift, we must believe in our hearts that Jesus saves us by the work He has already done on the cross.

Interview your church pastor. Ask him the following questions and record his answers.

Pastor's Name _____

How do you feel about Jesus being the only way to be saved?

_____

How do you know for sure that Jesus is alive?_____

_____

How old were you when you responded to the gospel and trusted in Jesus to save you? _____

_____

How have you felt God's love this week? _____

_____

How has the gospel changed your life?_____

_____

A journal is a place to keep track of your thoughts, feelings, questions, answers, and prayers. Use this page to write down what God is teaching you, any questions you have, or what you want to talk to God about.

WHAT NOW?

You just completed a Bible study of the gospel. *Gospel* just means "good news"! It is good news for those who believe. Think about it...**God rules**. He created us to be with Him and to bring Him glory, but **we sinned**. We messed up big time and disobeyed God. **God provided** His Son Jesus to live a perfect life and to be killed on the cross in our place for all our sins. Jesus took our punishment for us. Because of Jesus' life, death, and resurrection, we can now be a part of God's family and kingdom forever. **Jesus gives** us eternal life with Him. Now that's good news!

If you trust Jesus to save you and to be in charge of your life, you should know:

- Your sins are forgiven.
- You are a Christian.
- You are a child of God.
- God will always be with you through the Holy Spirit.
- You will go to heaven when you die.

Now, you should go and...

- Tell others (especially your parents) that you are a Christian.
- Talk with a trusted adult about baptism and how being baptized shows others that you have become a Christian.
- Find a church to attend. Get help from other Christians who love God and live for Him.
- Read the Bible to learn more about what it means to live for God.
- Talk to God every day. Praise God for who He is. Ask God to forgive you each time you mess up and to help you live for Him each day. Thank God for saving you through Jesus!
- Write about God saving you. This will remind you about God's work in your life and give you a way to tell others. Use the journal page on page 68 to write out your story of God saving you!

HOW TO STUDY THE BIBLE

STUDY ONE BIBLE BOOK.

1. Who wrote the book?
2. When was the book written?
3. What is the book about?
4. What does the book say about God?
5. What people does the book tell about?
6. How did the people act toward God?

STUDY ONE BIBLE VERSE.

1. Read the verse from different Bible translations.
2. What are the important words in the verse?
3. What are the words you don't understand?
4. Write the verse in your own words.
5. What can you learn from the verse?

STUDY ONE PERSON.

1. When and where did the person live?
2. What took place in the person's life?
3. How did the person act?
4. What can you learn from the person?

WRITE ABOUT IT!

What is God teaching you about Himself through this study? What have you learned about yourself? Have you responded to the gospel and trusted in Jesus? Is there anything you need to spend time talking to God about?

Use these journal pages to write out any thoughts or questions you have about what God is teaching you. If you've responded to the gospel and trusted in Jesus, write about how God saved you to remind you about God's work in your life and give you a way to tell others. Thank Him for teaching you through His Word.

SEARCH IT OUT!

Read and study the following verses from the Bible to learn more about what God says about the Gospel and His plan for you!

 ## GOD RULES.

Key Verse: "For everything was created by him, in heaven and on earth, the visible and the invisible, whether thrones or dominions or rulers or authorities—all things have been created through him and for him. He is before all things, and by him all things hold together." Colossians 1:16-17 (CSB)

Supporting Verses: Genesis 1:1; Revelation 4:11

 ## X WE SINNED.

Key Verse: "All have sinned and fall short of the glory of God." Romans 3:23 (CSB)

Supporting Verse: Romans 6:23

 ## GOD PROVIDED.

Key Verse: "You are saved by grace through faith, and this is not from yourselves; it is God's gift—not from works, so that no one can boast." Ephesians 2:8-9 (CSB)

Supporting Verse: John 3:16

JESUS GIVES.

Key Verse: "God proves his own love for us in that while we were still sinners, Christ died for us." Romans 5:8 (CSB)

Supporting Verses: 2 Corinthians 5:21; 1 Peter 3:18

 # WE RESPOND.

Key Verse: "If you confess with your mouth, 'Jesus is Lord,' and believe in your heart that God raised him from the dead, you will be saved." Romans 10:9 (CSB)

Supporting Verses: John 3:36; Acts 1:11; Romans 10:9-10, 13

THE GOSPEL & ME.

Key Verse: "Therefore, if anyone is in Christ, he is a new creation; the old has passed away, and see, the new has come!" 2 Corinthians 5:17 (CSB)

Supporting Verse: John 14:6

FAMILY GUIDE

Parents & Families,

What an exciting time in your life and the life of your child! There is nothing more important than your child grasping the truth of the gospel and trusting in Jesus. There is also no greater joy for you as a parent than the privilege of discipling your child in his or her faith. These pages will guide you as you help your child understand what it means to know and respond to the gospel and trust in Jesus as Savior and Lord.

Use this book each week. Set aside time to talk to your child about each session. Then, encourage your child to complete each daily devotion with you or on his or her own. Through this resource, you will help your child grow in faith and learn more about God's plan.

Session I
GOD RULES.

When we grasp the gospel, we discover that God created everything through Jesus and for Jesus. God is Creator, God rules, and He loves us.

Key Points. When we grasp the gospel, we discover that...

- God created everything through Jesus and for Jesus.
- God is Creator.
- God rules.
- God loves us.

Family Reading

Read Genesis 1:1-25 together as a family.

Discussion Questions

- What is your favorite thing God created?

- Do you like the beach or mountains better? Explain why.

- Do you enjoy watching a sunrise or a sunset more? Explain why.

- When you think of God as Creator, how would you describe Him?

- This week we learned that not only did God create all things, but He holds all things together. How does that make you feel?

Family Activity

Family Scavenger Hunt
This week, take time during your daily routine to mark off the things in God's creation that your family gets a chance to see using the "Family Scavenger Hunt" handout your child received. Encourage your child to bring the handout back to the next session and share his or her favorite part of creation with the group.

Session 2

 WE SINNED.

> When we grasp the gospel, we discover that we are sinners, and our sin separates us from God.

Key Points. When we grasp the gospel, we discover that...

- Sin is anything we think, say, or do that displeases God.
- We are sinners.
- Our sin separates us from God.
- God cannot ignore and must punish our sin.

Family Reading

Read Genesis 3:1-24.

Discussion Questions

- Summarize the Bible story in your own words.
- What do you think about what the serpent did?
- What was the consequence for Adam and Eve's disobedience?
- When someone has bad news and good news, which do you like to hear first?
- How do you feel about hearing that you are a sinner?

Family Activity

Scarlet Sin

Supplies: paper (1 piece per person), a red marker, crayon, pen

Instructions: With red marker, each family member will trace his or her hand on a piece of paper. Then everyone will write one or two sins they struggle with.

Note: Parents, it is important for your children to see and understand that you are also a sinner and struggle with sin.

Take time to share one of those sins with each other. Family members will switch their papers with another family member. Put your hands on their hand and pray for the sins that family member struggles with.

Session 3

GOD PROVIDED.

When we grasp the gospel, we discover that God provided the solution to our sin problem through faith in Christ alone.

Key Points. When we grasp the gospel, we discover that...

- Sin created a problem we cannot solve on our own.
- God provided the solution to our sin problem.
- Through faith in Jesus Christ alone, we can be rescued from our sin.

Family Reading

Read John 4:1-42.

Discussion Questions

- How would you have reacted if someone with a bad reputation talked to you in public?
- How did Jesus treat this woman?
- What was He offering that was different than what the well was offering?

- What is grace?
- How did Jesus show her grace and change her life?

Family Activity

John 3:16 Cards

Give each family member at least one key verse card received from session 3. Explain that they are to use their card to help memorize the key verse this week.

Session 4

JESUS GIVES.

When we grasp the gospel, we discover that we must turn from self and sin to Jesus and believe in our hearts that Jesus saves us by the work He has already done on the cross.

Key Points. When we grasp the gospel, we discover that...

- To *repent* means to turn from our sinful way and go God's way.
- We can be welcomed into God's family by believing in our hearts that Jesus saves us by what He has already done on the cross.
- We can't keep this news to ourselves; we have to share the good news of Jesus with others.

Family Reading

Read Matthew 27:32-44.

Discussion Questions

- How do you feel after reading these Scripture verses?
- What would you have done if you were forced to carry Jesus' cross for Him?
- How do you feel about how Jesus was treated while He was hanging on the cross?
- Why did Jesus have to die?

Family Activity

Jesus Paid for Sin

Supplies: ice cubes (one for each family member)

Give family members each an ice cube and challenge them to hold it on the inside of their wrist as long as they can. After a while the cold will start to hurt a little. Take the ice off the wrists before anyone is hurt.

Ask: What did it feel like after the ice was on your wrist for a long time?

This was a simple experience that was uncomfortable for a moment. Jesus suffered and died on the cross to take our punishment for sin.

Session 5
WE RESPOND.

When we grasp the gospel, we discover that God's gift of Jesus is the only way to be saved. To receive this gift, we must believe in our hearts that Jesus saves us by the work He has already done on the cross.

Key Points. When we grasp the gospel, we discover that...

- There is only one way to be saved—Jesus.
- Jesus, the gift of God, is the greatest gift we have ever been given, but we must respond to receive this gift.
- We can be welcomed into God's family by believing in our hearts that Jesus saves us by what He has already done on the cross.

Family Reading

Read John 3:1-21.

Discussion Questions

- How would you describe Nicodemus?
- What was Jesus trying to explain to Nicodemus?
- In your own words, describe what you think it means to be born again.
- Read John 3:16 together as a family.

Family Activity

Part of the Family

Pull out family photos and talk about the day your children became a part of the family. That might be the day they were born, the day they were adopted, or the day they came into your home. Share your feelings on that day, how things happened, and any special moments.

Explain that as special as that day was, it doesn't compare to how special it is to respond to the gospel and trust in Jesus (be born again). Make sure your kids understand that they do not have to become a baby and be born again, but that when they are born again in the Spirit, they receive God's forgiveness. They are rescued from their sin and welcomed into the family of God.

Session 6

THE GOSPEL AND ME.

When we grasp the gospel, we discover that God Rules, We Sinned, God Provided, Jesus Gives, and We Respond. These gospel truths are personal, life-changing, and can make us into a new creation.

Key Points. When we grasp the gospel we discover that:

- The good news is: God Rules, We Sinned, God Provided, Jesus Gives, and We Respond.
- In Christ we are new creations; the old has gone, the new has come.
- We can't keep this news to ourselves; we have to share the good news of Jesus with others.

Family Reading

Read Romans 10:9-10,13.

Discussion Questions

- What do these verses tell us we need to do to be saved?
- What is salvation?
- Who does Jesus save?
- Has Jesus saved you?

Family Activity

Share Your Story

Adults or other family members that have trusted in Jesus, this is a great time to tell your story. Make it a special night. Throw a blanket down, circle up, and share how you found Jesus. Allow your children to ask you questions. Share with them Scripture verses that are important to you and why.

CERTIFICATE OF COMPLETION

this certificate is awarded to

Evelyn or Evelyn

(NAME)

on

February 26 - 23 - 00

(DATE)

FOR COMPLETING

The Gospel: God's Plan For Me

PARENT OR GUARDIAN SIGNATURE

THE GOSPEL

God's Plan For Me

GOD RULES.

The Bible tells us God created everything, including you and me, and He is in charge of everything. Genesis 1:1; Revelation 4:11; Colossians 1:16-17

WE SINNED.

We all choose to disobey God. The Bible calls this sin. Sin separates us from God and deserves God's punishment of death. Romans 3:23; 6:23

GOD PROVIDED.

God sent Jesus, the perfect solution to our sin problem, to rescue us from the punishment we deserve. It's something we, as sinners, could never earn on our own. Jesus alone saves us. John 3:16; Ephesians 2:8-9

JESUS GIVES.

He lived a perfect life, died on the cross for our sins, and rose again. Because Jesus gave up His life for us, we can be welcomed into God's family for eternity. This is the best gift ever! Romans 5:8; 2 Corinthians 5:21; 1 Peter 3:18; Ephesians 2:8-9

WE RESPOND.

Believe in your heart that Jesus alone saves you through what He's already done on the cross. Repent, turning from self and sin to Jesus. Tell God and others that your faith is in Jesus. John 14:6; Romans 10:9-10,13